D1630296

Sleep Tight, Little Wolf

İyi uykular, küçük kurt

A picture book in two languages

GREENWICH LIBRARIES

3 8028 02505948 3

Ulrich Renz · Barbara Brinkmann

Sleep Tight, Little Wolf

İyi uykular, küçük kurt

Translation:

Pete Savill (English)

Şerife Aydoğmuş (Turkish)

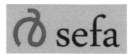

Download audiobook at:

www.sefa-bilingual.com/mp3

Password for free access:

English: **LWEN1423**

Turkish: **henüz mevcut değil sesli kitap**

(audio not yet available)

We are working on making as many of our bilingual books as possible available as audiobooks. If there is no audio version in your language yet, please be patient! You can check our „Language Wizard" for the latest updates: www.sefa-bilingual.com/languages

Good night, Tim! We'll continue searching tomorrow.
Now sleep tight!

İyi geceler Tim, yarın aramaya devam ederiz.
Şimdi güzelce uyu!

It is already dark outside.

Hava karardı.

What is Tim doing?

Peki Tim ne yapıyor?

He is leaving for the playground.

What is he looking for there?

Dışarı çıkıyor, parka gidiyor.

Orda aradığı nedir?

The little wolf!

He can't sleep without it.

Küçük peluş kurdu!

Onsuz uyuyamıyor.

Who's this coming?

Kimdir şurdan gelen?

Marie! She's looking for her ball.

Marie! O da topunu arıyor.

And what is Tobi looking for?

Tobi ne arıyor peki?

His digger.

Vinçini.

And what is Nala looking for?

Peki Nala ne arıyor?

Her doll.

Bebeğini.

Don't the children have to go to bed?

The cat is rather surprised.

Çoçukların yatağa gitmeleri gerekmiyor mu?

Kedi çok şaşırıyor.

Who's coming now?

Şimdi kim geliyor?

Tim's mum and dad!

They can't sleep without their Tim.

Tim'in Annesi ve Babası!

Tim olmadan uyuyamıyorlar.

More of them are coming! Marie's dad.

Tobi's grandpa. And Nala's mum.

Bir çok kişi daha geliyor! Marie'nin Babası.

Tobi'nin Dedesi. Ve Nala'nın Annesi.

Now hurry to bed everyone!

Hadi ama çabuk yatağa!

Good night, Tim!

Tomorrow we won't have to search any longer.

İyi geceler, Tim!

Sabahleyin aramak zorunda değiliz artık.

Sleep tight, little wolf!

İyi uykular, küçük kurt!

Dear Reader,

Thanks for choosing my book! If you (and most of all, your child) liked it, please spread the word via a Facebook-Like or an email to your friends:

www.sefa-bilingual.com/like

I would also be happy to get a comment or a review. Likes and comments are great „Tender Loving Care" for authors, thanks so much!

If there is no audiobook version in your language yet, please be patient! We are working on making all the languages available as audiobooks. You can check the „Language Wizard" for the latest updates:

www.sefa-bilingual.com/languages

Now let me briefly introduce myself: I was born in Stuttgart in 1960, together with my twin brother Herbert (who also became a writer). I studied French literature and a couple of languages in Paris, then medicine in Lübeck. However, my career as a doctor was brief because I soon discovered books: medical books at first, for which I was an editor and a publisher, and later non-fiction and children's books.

I live with my wife Kirsten in Lübeck in the very north of Germany; together we have three (now grown) children, a dog, two cats, and a little publishing house: Sefa Press.

If you want to know more about me, you are welcome to visit my website: **www.ulrichrenz.de**

Best regards,

Ulrich Renz

The illustrator

Barbara Brinkmann was born in Munich in 1969 and grew up in the foothills of the Bavarian Alps. She studied architecture in Munich and is currently a research associate in the Department of Architecture at the Technical University of Munich. She also works as a freelance graphic designer, illustrator, and author.

www.bcbrinkmann.de

Do you like drawing?

Here are the pictures from the story to color in:

www.sefa-bilingual.com/coloring

Enjoy!

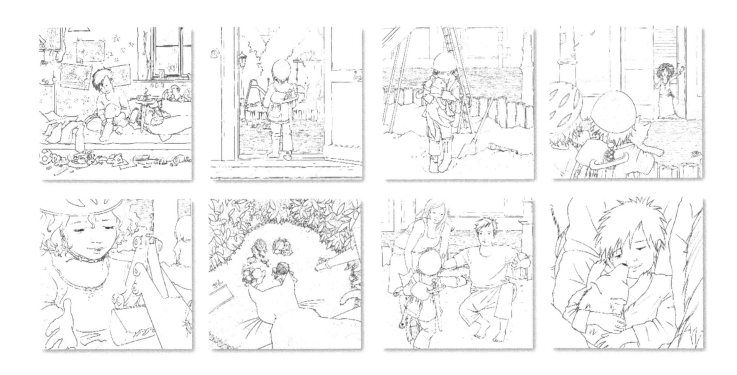

Little Wolf also recommends:

Ulrich Renz · Marc Robitzky

The Wild Swans
Yaban kuğuları

Based on a fairy tale by
Hans Christian Andersen

sefa

English — bilingual — Turkish

The Wild Swans

Based on a fairy tale by
Hans Christian Andersen

▶ Recommended age: 4-5 and up

„The Wild Swans" by Hans Christian Andersen is, with good reason, one of the world's most popular fairy tales. In its timeless form it addresses the issues out of which human dramas are made: fear, bravery, love, betrayal, separation and reunion.

Available in your languages?

▶ Check out with our „Language Wizard":

www.sefa-bilingual.com/languages

My Most Beautiful Dream

► Recommended age: 3-4
and up

Lulu can't fall asleep. All her cuddly toys are dreaming already – the shark, the elephant, the little mouse, the dragon, the kangaroo, and the lion cub. Even the bear has trouble keeping his eyes open ...
Hey bear, will you take me along into your dream?
Thus begins a journey for Lulu that leads her through the dreams of her cuddly toys – and finally to her own most beautiful dream.

Available in your languages?

► Check out with our „Language Wizard":

www.sefa-bilingual.com/languages

Visit us!
www.sefa-bilingual.com

More of me ...

Bo & Friends

► Children's detective series in three volumes. Reading age: 9+

► German Edition: „Motte & Co" ► www.motte-und-co.de

► Download the series' first volume, „Bo and the Blackmailers" for free!

www.bo-and-friends.com/free

© 2020 by Sefa Verlag Kirsten Bödeker, Lübeck, Germany

www.sefa-verlag.de

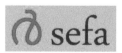

IT: Paul Bödeker, Freiburg, Germany

Font: Noto Sans

All rights reserved. No part of this book may be reproduced without the written consent of the publisher.

ISBN: 9783739913568

Version: 20190101

Lightning Source UK Ltd.
Milton Keynes UK
UKHW050329220722
406189UK00005B/199

9 783739 913568